Sea Stories:
The Scuttlebutt Chronicles

written by: James Wells

and

illustrated by: Dymond Renea

RoseDog Books
PITTSBURGH, PENNSYLVANIA 15238

RoseDog Books
585 Alpha Drive
Suite 103
Pittsburgh, PA 15238
Visit our website at *www.rosedogbookstore.com*

ISBN: 978-1-64913-052-5
eISBN: 978-1-64913-067-9

Welcome, sit back and relax as I take you on a hilarious adventure throughout time with some of the craziest people and places in the world. Although this book is based on actual stories, some of the things you will read will have you scratching your head, laughing till your stomach hurts, and being thankful that you don't act like that or do those crazy things yourself... or do you?

STORIES

Sea Stories:
The Scuttlebutt Chronicles

NEW ID CARD

Getting an ID card is a necessity in our everyday lives. You need one to get into some businesses, apply for different products, and different services throughout your life will require that ID card. Before we get into the meat and potatoes, I'd like to take a moment to talk to you about ID card people customer service. Let me paint a few pictures for you, and I'll let you try to figure out what's going on here. So there's this guy that has an ID card that is about to expire. Like any normal person, he went down to the ID lab to get a new ID card. They hooked him up, and he did get a new ID card, but they kept the expiration date of the old card on it. Yes, you read that correctly, his new ID card still expires in less than a week from the day he went to get the new card.

It's like standing in line at the DMV for twelve hours trying to renew your car registration and they tell you, "We will send it to you in the mail." So when you get your new registration in the mail, it's the same exact dates that are already on your car, then you get a notice in the mail a day later saying your registration is expired and you need to renew it, but now there's a late fee because it's overdue. Logbooks would be a great way to manage information like this to make sure the dates get changed properly.

SKYDIVING INTO A POOL

L ogbooks are a great idea. They are the perfect way to track and manage things, such as dates, times, and other pertinent information like the accounting of people, so that they make it back safely and on time. The only problem is the block that was supposed to be for check in date and time, someone put an actual check mark in all the blocks instead of the date. Not really sure how "date/time in" and a check mark correlates but sure. It's important to make sure everyone is accounted for on time. If not it could result in one of those days when you wake up in Australia at like 1 A.M. because you just can't sleep, and by chance, happen to go out to the balcony for some fresh air and see a guy yeet from the tenth floor of a hotel into a three foot pool. Not sure what was going through this guy's mind as he plummeted below, but he looked as afraid as a guy with diarrhea looking for toilet paper during a virus outbreak. The sound of the tsunami he created in the pool was louder than Grandpa's lime green Sunday tie. After making a ruckus loud enough to wake half the people in the city, the hotel security finally decided to investigate what was going on. As the security guard was trying to help the guy who we will refer to as Lieutenant Dan due to his two broken legs he received upon entering the pool from the tenth floor. Lieutenant Dan started pulling himself along the side of the pool, cursing at the security guard telling him how if he wants to get him out of the pool, he needs to come in and get him. About fifteen minutes went by with the security guard following Dan around the pool. When out of nowhere, Dan started screaming out a bunch of funny words. Moments later the paramedics showed up, pulled him out of the pool, and escorted him to the nearest medical treatment facility where he was treated for his pride and his wounds. Sky diving into a pool is not the only way injuries happen.

SINGAPORE SWINGER

I once took a trip to Singapore, and a guy got drunk on the first day of my visit. He tried to take some "girl" in a cab with him. Unfortunately as he was hugged up on her in the cab, that was not a flashlight he felt in the side of his hip. He found out the hard way it was a man and beat the fake boobs out of shim. Really lumped him up rather good. After the decimation of the lady boy, he had to get rid of all the witnesses. So what better witness to beat up than the cab driver who was driving them around. It's like that time your little brother watched you drink the milk out the cartoon, and you were worried that he was going to tell Mom, but he really wasn't, so you beat him up just in case. Then he told Mom you hit him, and because his pride was hurt, he told her that you drank the milk, also, so you got a whooping for the milk anyway. Well, this is the same thing, except now you're drunk, in a foreign country, and there's no little brother and there's no milk. So next time you decide to hang out in Singapore, make sure you check for Adam's apples and birth certificates.

CHOCO TACO

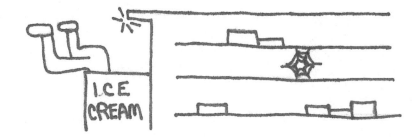

S peaking of apples, have you ever been so hungry that you would risk life and limb for a Choco Taco? This story takes place in the corner store, where a very hungry person was browsing the barren shelves looking for something to eat as if he was Tom Hanks in the movie *Cast Away*. While looking around, he decides to look in the freezer, and to his delight, what does he find sitting there waiting for those massive meat hooks to reach in and grab? The LAST Choco Taco. Now you could tell from the glimmer in his eyes that he was happier than a junkie in an OxyContin factory. So as his arm reached in the freezer, going about fifty-seven miles per hour as if he were saving a child from falling off a bridge, he smacked his head on the top shelf above the freezer, nearly rendering himself unconscious. As he lifted himself up, dazed and looking as if he has a concussion with blood running down the side of his head. The guy at the counter asked him if he's alright. He then looked down at his hand and saw that he was still able to grab the Choco Taco first try.

He then looked back up at the clerk and said, "I'm good now," as he proceeded to pay for the item and slowly stumbled out of the store. What's worse is he was the only person in the store, so he didn't have to hit the freezer like a maddened shopper on Black Friday. He could have simply reached in like a civilized person and got what he wanted with no problems. At least he was lucky enough to have a choice to get some food he actually wanted.

THE WONDERFUL WORLD OF EGGS

I went down to a buffet for breakfast one morning, and they were serving two types of eggs. They had the egg bake, which consisted of a bunch of vegetables that nobody wanted to eat, so they mixed it in with the eggs. Eating that stuff was worse than going to a funeral. They also had what appeared to be boiled eggs, which had the consistency of a Jello shot when you broke it open, but I guess that's what happens when you boil eggs in an oven. This wasn't the only mix up that happened that beautiful Monday morning. They also mixed up the pancake batter with cement. The pancakes were crunchier than Doritos. It literally cracked the corner of the plate with its durability. Even though the pancakes were tougher than an over cooked steak, I still would rather eat that than go a few days eating only bread and water.

BREAD AND WATER

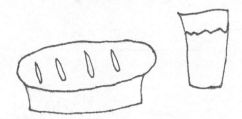

Diets usually help people out when they want to shed a few pounds. There are many types to choose from as well. One of the less known diets you probably should try not to do is eating only bread and drinking water. Regardless what diet you do end up trying, don't go overboard with it like this guy did. While spending his three-day, three-night smorgasbord in the comfort of his home, this guy decided it would be a great idea to shoot for the record for the most bread eaten in a three-day period. Unbeknownst to him that when you eat thirty-five plus slices of bread and sop up more water than a sponge in that short amount of time, it will clog you up faster than the time it takes to win a knife fight in a phone booth. The day he completed his diet, he went to the doctors to get some laxatives, but they weren't working fast enough. So that night, he decided to take matters in his own hands, or should I say fingers. His roommate, who was in the living room walking by, happened to hear some strange grunting noises coming from a room in the back, and to his surprise, he witnessed the bread and water guy sticking everything from broom stick handles to fingers in his booty hole trying to dislodge the blockage. Now you would think something like this would be an isolated incident. Unfortunately this isn't the only crazy thing that has happened when you have roommates.

CHECK YOUR HEADPHONES

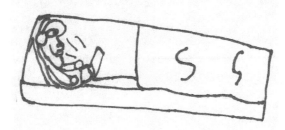

hink of that time when you went to college and had a huge dorm room. But this dorm doesn't have any walls. The only thing separating you from everyone else was a tiny thin curtain. But this was home. This was a place you could usually go after work and school to unwind and relax, get some sleep, or watch some videos. You know how it is after a long day at work. Well, this dude thought it was his prime opportunity to dive deep into his uninhibited desires with his illegally downloaded porn collection from LimeWire. I'm assuming this guy had it all planned out. He probably picked out the best of the best while fantasizing about being in a candlelit bathtub with a glass of red wine. Little did he know his headphones were unplugged and the volume was turned all the way up. It also didn't help that the dorm was full of people who just got done with their shift trying to get settled in as well.

While everyone was sitting on the couch watching macho movies, like *Training Day* and *Rambo*, a female's voice could be heard in the background saying, "Give it to me, daddy, yes, yes, harder, harder," from behind one of the curtains. Confused, the guys on the couch did what guys who hear sexy female voices do best and investigated the disturbance and strange noises. They found the noise and the curtain expeditiously. Things sounded like they were getting hot and heavy. Not wanting to spoil the current festivities taking place or anything, one of the guys beat the living hell out of the side of the locker next to the curtain as if they were the DEA during a drug raid, telling the offender to knock that crap off. Things got incredibly quiet and awkwardly silent after that.

NO IRON BOARD, NO PROBLEM

Awkward can come in so many sizes, shapes, and forms. Sometimes it's socially, other times it's just straight up strange, like the guy who was at work and had to be in his nicest uniform that day for a ceremony. He walked in, and his uniform looked as if it was ironed with a pillowcase full of rocks. His uniform looked like a finger that been in a cup of water for fifteen hours. So of course, he was told to go back home and iron it and hurry back in twenty minutes, so he could get everything ready. He ran back to his house and happened to bump into a few of his roommates. Panicking he was telling them he had to iron his uniform quickly. Therefore his friends, being the good Samaritans they were, came up with this elaborate idea that hey, we should just iron your uniform with you still wearing it, this way we can save some time and you can get back to work faster. They did, and the guy came back to work. But this time he wasn't as happy as he was the first time and was actually quite mad. You could tell by how red his skin was. He was redder than an albino on *Survivor*. His uniform now had patches and burn marks all over the sleeves, and he had this look on his face, like I had no choice but to be ironed in my clothes. Ironically, pun definitely intended, ironing your clothes while wearing them isn't the only way to get burned doing routine things.

MELTING IN THE SHOWER

I magine trying to do something as routine as getting clean after a long day, and while your shower starts off like a normal routine thing and you got soap all on your face, the atmosphere suddenly shifts. Next thing you know, your leg is melting. While trying to avoid temperatures rivaling that of the sun, you try to get out of the way but because you can't see with the soap in your eyes, all you know is that someone just set the entire bathroom on fire. You try to get out of the way the best you can, but it just isn't working. My strategy was I'll throw my leg backwards to get it out of the water and as I did, my heel caught a rivet sticking out on the metal wall of the shower. As I stood there now bleeding out, in pain, and in need of a tourniquet, I tried to turn off the water by the knob, but the handle was also hotter than a Sports Illustrated swimsuit calendar. Liquid lava was literally pouring out the shower head onto my already abused body. I'm pretty sure I burned all the fingerprints off my hand as the valve was also hotter than a nipple slip at a Superbowl Halftime show. Any hotter and the water would have melted a hole in the bathroom floor. Eventually the water equaled out for me to rinse the soap off, but showering sometimes on a cruise ship was an experience in itself.

SLEEP ADVICE

D ays like that make you want to just go to sleep and not think about it, but it's not always easy to fall asleep near a construction site for various reasons, loud noises, small beds, flat pillows, the list goes on. It gets annoying sometimes to the point you decide to go to the doctor and get some professional advice. Sometimes that advice isn't always what you want to hear. While having issues with getting some sleep and staying asleep, a guy went down to their doctor's office for his sleep study appointment. While in there, he told the doc he was having some insomnia symptoms. The doc started asking a bunch of questions to see how this guy's sleeping habits were, and he asked if he drank any coffee or energy drinks daily. The guy told him no, he doesn't drink that crap. The doc basically then tells the guy that he is the reason why all the vending machines in the area are sold out of Red Bull and Monster energy drinks. The doc then suggested that the best possible solution to fix this guy's sleeping issue is to not shower before bed because this will reset his internal clock. This is like telling someone with a broken toe to wear a helmet next time. The doc also suggests he try some things on a paper that he handed him from a Pinterest printout.

He told him, "Yeah, most of these don't apply to us because we are near all this construction, but try the ones you can, and after two weeks if nothing is working, then try to deprive yourself of even more sleep, so that you are to the point of exhaustion. This way you can fall asleep with no problem." Is this really the cure to insomnia? So after the appointment is done, he prescribes melatonin and he says, "Oh, I almost forgot, hop up on that table, so I can check your lungs and heart because I'm supposed to do that." He almost forgot to take vitals.

WRONG DIAGNOSIS

octor visits like that reminds me of that time this guy who was complaining about his shoulder throbbing all week. He went to the doctors to get looked over and repaired, and about thirty minutes had passed, and he ended up coming back to work. Everyone is standing there looking at him like, you're back already, so what happened. He told everyone that he went to the doctor and explained to the doc that his shoulder was hurting, and he thinks he might have slept on it wrong or tore something. The doctor ran a quick vital check on him and told him he had a lower back injury. Then they sent him to the pharmacy to get medicine for a headache. With the look of confusion on his face, as if he victimized with his show me on this Barbie doll where the bad man touched you face, he sat there helplessly as they wrote him a prescription for Motrin and sent him on his way. This almost sounds as bad as giving Batman a coupon for new parents, but the coupon is expired. It's just like that time your garbage disposal stopped working, so you replaced your bathtub to fix the problem.

CORRESPONDENCE BIN

Doctors are typically good, but sometimes they seem about as useful as nipples on an armored breastplate. Do you know what else is useless? Good idea fairies. The ones that say they don't like the way the metal correspondence bin, that's sturdy and works perfectly fine, looks. Therefore they have you take it off and put up a flimsy plastic one, something that looks great but is about as functional as a bucket with a hole in it. This new plastic correspondence bin was taped to the side of the cabinet and kept falling down. The old bin that never fell was metal, screwed in, and never had any durability issues. This new plastic bin couldn't even hold a box of Kleenex before it fell and hit the floor. So every night, it would fall down, we would pick it up, and sit it to the side. The next shift would come in and put it back on the cabinet but with even more double-sided tape than it was the previous day. Had to have been an entire roll of duct tape holding this thing up one night. This thing couldn't even hold a ruler, so it definitely wasn't about to hold them twenty-nine folders they keep putting in it. However, this wasn't the only box that was taped to the side of something. Every single box in the room was replaced and now had this same engineering deficiency. It really was a mess. But do you know what else can be a mess? Classified ads. Classified ads can usually have some decent things people try to give away or sell, but sometimes you see things in the classifieds that have you scratching your head, wondering just how bad their struggle is.

CHICKEN SAUCE

While scrolling through the classified ads, one item that caught my eye was a bottle of Chic-Fil-A sauce that was being auctioned off to the highest bidder, and the bid had gotten up to $40 for an eight ounce container. For that price, I would hope it came with a sandwich genie that appears when you rub the side of the container and makes a chicken sandwich for you. The fact that someone was willing to pay that much instead of just ordering their own, having someone send them some or just wait until they got to a Chic-Fil-A tells you a lot about how much people value seasonings, condiments, and tasteful food. I've seen things placed on food trays that looked like the plot from a horror film. Things that would give your nightmares bad dreams, like macaroni and cheese with raisins or grapes in it. Or like that time I got a piece of chicken, and when I cut it open, it looked like I snipped an artery. Blood squirted all over the guy next to me as if I were performing unlicensed heart surgery on a hitch hiker. Surprised it didn't jump up on the table and start running around knocking over all the Tapatio bottles.

AUK

Most nightmares happen in your dreams, but sometimes nightmares can frighten you while you're awake. Have you ever had to use the bathroom so badly that you didn't care about anything else, such as safety, health, or the condition you would be left sitting in vulnerable? Neither have I, but that is exactly what happened next. There was this bathroom that hands down had to be the most disgusting place on planet earth that you've ever seen or smelled. Personally I was afraid to go in this bathroom in the fear of walking around the corner and getting punched in the face by Hepatitis A, B, and C. I mean, even the toilet looked like it was HIV positive. There are literally lower intestines that were cleaner than this bathroom. This place was dirtier than Bill Cosby's browser history. But apparently for some random guy, using the facility was no problem. In fact this guy decided he was just going to sit down and do his thing. I have never seen any toilet paper in this bathroom, so it makes you wonder what he used. So after the roaring sound of a flush was heard, the door opened, and the guy walked out the bathroom without washing his hands, touching everything in site on his way out the door. Even if he wanted to wash his hands, there was no soap in the dispenser, but from the lack of hesitation, you could clearly see that washing his hands never crossed his mind. Just throw him and the entire room away. Just make sure that when you throw the room and him away, you don't throw them over the side of a cruise ship, or man overboard may get called away.

HUMAN TRASH BAG

Man overboard on a cruise ship or any ship is not to be taken lightly, nor is it a laughing matter. But some people just want to watch the world burn. At two o'clock in the morning, most people are asleep from a hard-long day of work, enjoyment, or sight-seeing. While most were asleep in their beds, another guy was wide awake crafting body parts out of trash and piecing them together to look like a human. Once he finished with his human-shaped trash bag, he decided to give it even more flare and attach a tee shirt and a glow stick to it, so now you could see it really good in the dark. Curious to see if this Frankenstein trash bag could swim, he threw it over the side and watched as it floated away. He was not the only one watching this body float away. The guy on watch who rang the alarm at 2 A.M., waking up all the people on the ship to take roll call, also saw this fake body holding a glow stick. It's bad when this happens the first time, but after several nights of man overboard false alarms, the Captain put a bounty out for the guy. Requesting for anyone that has any information leading to the apprehension of this menacing bandit to come forward. Thankfully there were no other human-shaped trash bag sightings the rest of the cruise.

THREE BEST FRIENDS

I magine being a real person that fell in the water. This was actually remarkably close to happening. While working on a flight deck of any ship, there are several dangers a human must look out for. Falling off the ship, aircraft propellers, and the most common danger...when a guy walks behind a plane on the catapult and it knocks him down like a credit score when you've maxed out all your credit cards and didn't pay your bills for five months. After he slid across the ground in what appeared to be a slow motion scene from *The Matrix*, he was able to cling to a small hole on the elevator, saving himself from sliding off the side of the ship and into the deep blue abyss. As most people were looking at this situation unfold and realizing he just had to wait for the plane to fly away before he could get up. Three guys decided they needed to intervene and pick their buddy up off the ground while the plane was still getting ready to take off. Plop went the first guy, ker plunk, the second followed by a yeet from the third, all now sliding across the ground past the original guy holding on to his foot tighter than a condom on an elephant. After the plane flew off, they were taken inside. And that was the last time anyone saw those guys ever again. Maybe it would have been better to just let go when they had the chance.

THE FIRE TRUCK IS ON FIRE

When events like this happen, it's a good thing emergency responder vehicles are on the scene ready to fight the fight. But just like cars, sometimes fire trucks break down to the point where their engine no longer works properly and needs to be replaced. After replacing an engine, you have to fill it back up with all the fluids and hook up all the electrical wires. So after everything was hooked up and ready to go, these guys tried to crank it up to make sure everything was working properly. Well, the driver was not aware of who was in the back of the vehicle and started cranking it up as if he was a man with a mission. After realizing nothing was happening, he finally decided to look back because of the loud sound of cooking popcorn near the batteries. Next thing you know, all he saw was sparks and fire. The guy in the back was waving his arms like a wacky wavy inflatable tube man trying to tell the guy to turn it off. The guy in the passenger's seat jumped down and ran to the back where the fire was. The driver then ran right past an actual fire fighter who kept walking as if he was blinder than Clayton Bigsby at a KKK rally. So instead of grabbing the CO_2 bottle that was near the passenger's seat, he ran about 120 feet to grab a different one and emptied it faster than a man leaving his girlfriend after hearing the pregnancy results. As soon as the fire was out, everyone seemed to find their eyes because they all started to see what was happening. Fires are just one of the many dangers in the world you have to worry about. Even something as simple as sitting down a toolbox can lead to a bad day.

A JACK, A HELICOPTER, AND A TOOLBOX

So a jack, a helicopter, and a toolbox walk into an aircraft hangar, and if I were to ask you, who do you think would win between the toolbox and the helicopter? Who would you put your money on? If you said aircraft, well, let's just see what actually happened. Just like every other day where the maintenance folks are doing their maintenance, they had to lift the back part of the helicopter to do some repairs. When they jack up the back of it, the front part lowers. It's the same way how a seesaw works. Well, before they start to jack it up, they walk around and make sure nothing is in the way. This way they don't damage the aircraft. They did their walk around and nothing was in the way, all clear and all good to go, so they started to lift the back. Meanwhile another guy doing maintenance on something else was walking through the hangar with a giant bright white toolbox. He decided that out of the entire soccer field sized hangar, the best possible spot for him to set his toolbox down would be right in front of the only helicopter that was having repairs done. CRUNCH. Toolbox = 1, Helicopter = 0. Not sure who in Wakanda makes those toolboxes, but any toolbox that can get crushed, put a giant hole in a helicopter, and look perfectly fine afterwards, I want one. I guess next time they should do some reverification to ensure they aren't making million-dollar mistakes.

VERIFRIBATION

et's give some consideration to the word verification for a moment. It can often be used to ensure that something was done properly. That being said, what word is used to describe a verification of a verification to verify something that was verified already? Well, there isn't one, but if there was, you could safely assume it would be along the lines of verifribation (Ver-If-Ri-bayshun) (verb), meaning you rigorously verify something to the point of exhaustion and chapping skin. A maintenance guy was inspecting two tires that he received and noticed that one of the tires had the wrong bearing in it and the other had the right bearing in it. So he said go ahead and install the good one and take the other one back to the store and get another one. Easy peasy. Common sense tells you that if the guy got two tires and he found a discrepancy on one of them, then he obviously looked for the same thing on the other to make sure both of them were good before putting his name on the paperwork and installing it on an the vehicle. So even though he verified it as good, that was not good enough. He decided that he would take that tire off of the vehicle, tear it completely down, and inspect it again. Then put all new parts on it. That's like vacuuming up your living room, then ripping up your carpet to make sure you got all the dirt underneath, then laying it back down and re-vacuuming up your carpet again afterwards. After taking the tire apart, they had one person build it, had another person watch him build it, and then had another person watch the watcher watch him build it to verify that this tire was put back together the right way (again), then put it back on the vehicle. It's like going to Starbucks and ordering four drinks, and one of the drinks had the wrong lid, so they apologize and ask for all the drinks back, pour them all down the drain, and start over again. You get all your drinks about ten and half hours later because they ran out of coffee verifying that everyone's drinks in the store were made correctly. It's seems like enough to drive you nuts and make you want to do something crazy. Something like jumping off a pier into a foreign river or something.

GOING FOR A SWIM

Have you ever just sat on a pier waiting for a boat to pick you up and wonder what it would be like to just take off all your clothes and jump in the water? YOLO. Well, sit down, pour yourself a cup of coffee, and I'll tell you all about it. While waiting on the pier for his boat to pick him up, some guy decided it would be a great idea to strip down half naked and cannonball off the pier into the water while waiting for the boat to arrive. He must have gotten tired of waiting and decided he'd swim the two plus miles back to the ship in the dark. A group of people dove in the water after him, but his inner Michael Phelps kicked in as he started to back stroke away from them and hide under the pier. It's like the movie *Shawshank Redemption*, in the scene when he was trying to escape through the pipe, except everyone knows what pipe he's in. So while he's under the pier, everyone is running back and forth to both sides of the pier trying to find this guy.

One guy said, "Lean over and look, don't worry, bro, I got your legs," as he almost dropped that guy in the water, too. So while everyone is in the water playing Marco Polo, this guy swims out from under the pier towards the gate as if he is about to go back out in town like he didn't just cause a scene. Meanwhile all the Vietnamese boats and search and rescue people are still in the water madder than a three-legged dog trying to bury a turd on an icy pond. Some say he was trying to catch an octopus he saw in the water. Some say he was trying to mount an escape and never return. And some say he was trying to save his locally and illegally procured monkey Gerald from drowning. It could have been worse though. Instead of trying out for the swim team, he could have tried out for something more extravagant, like Olympic ice-skating.

THE ICE SKATER

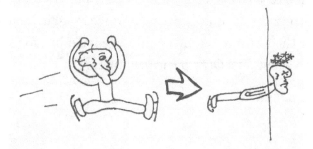

W hile enjoying our time in the Philippines, many people were able to do several different leisurely things that included tours, drinking, malls, and other such activities. One guy decided having never been ice skating before that he would give it a try. During his Olympic debut, he put on his ice-skates, just like he would do at work, and proceeded to get on the ice. The first lap was no problem, easy day. But the second lap is where tragedy would strike. In an attempt to perform his best impersonation of a triple axel, he Charlie Browned, followed it up with a stanky leg and a wobble wop, slipped, fell, and slid across the ice on his face. After getting up wounded, bloody, and vulnerable with his eyebrow leaking worse than a hand me down diaper, the local medical team at the facility took a piece of cotton that appeared to be as thin as a piece of notebook paper and taped it to his eye. After using an entire roll of masking tape and having him look like a pirate, he came back to the cruise ship where America's favorite world-class medical team removed his eye patch and proceed to wrap his entire forehead up with an ACE bandage. After looking at the size of his bandage, it would appear as though he really sliced his head up

James Wells

pretty bad, but Maury had determined that to be a lie, as he only received a few stitches right above his eyebrow. Falling on ice skates isn't the only thing that can give you boo boos. Fighting random people or objects, such as ATM machines, can also lead to injury.

LADY BOYS AND ATMS

Working in an engine room can be a lot of hard and demanding work. Long hours, crappy work rotations, and constantly working in extremely hot temperatures. So when given the opportunity to let their hair down in a foreign port, you would think the cruise line employees would just chill and relax or enjoy their time. Maybe even go out and meet some local people. While out in town, one guy thought it would be a good idea to link up with a girl on his buddies Tinder account. Well, in the Philippines, there are three types of people you will meet: You have your men, your women, and then what is referred to as the lady boys. So as you already figured out, this guy was talking to a lady boy. After meeting up and realizing she wasn't who he thought she was, he tried to leave.

Well, apparently the lady boy wasn't done with him yet and decided to blackmail him and say, "Well, if you don't pay me $2,000, I am going to tell the police on you." That didn't go over too well with the guy as he proceeded to pulverize the lady boy's face. But he wasn't the only engine room guy who decided to get in fisticuffs and let off a little steam. Engine room guy number two tried to use an

ATM machine, but the machine decided to DEBO him and basically said I'm not going to give you any money or your card back, and there is nothing you can do about it. So what did this guy do? He started to rage out and punched the ATM right in the face. He continued beating the ATM machine to a bloody pulp. Clearly this guy was a few fries short of a happy meal. Meanwhile as the story goes, there was a man standing in line waiting to use the ATM machine next. That man happened to be an undercover agent. Talk about being in the right place at the wrong time. Fortunately for him, he only suffered minor injuries. Good thing we had such an amazing medical team that was able to patch up his hand and get him on his way. Medical people always have your best interest in mind, especially when it comes to things that can get you sick. In fact I would like to take a little time to talk about some information that our medical staff provided us with one time.

MOSQUITO BOUNDARIES

So information went out about malaria prophylaxis in the Philippines, however, the information was only concerning people who were going outside of the designated boundary area. I guess mosquitos don't bother you if you are staying in bounds while out in town. #winning, only the people going out of bounds need to worry about mosquitos. It gets better when it said you are "strongly encouraged" to come to medical, but not for the medicine that is similar to a flu shot that "may or may not work." You will come down for a screening to see if you will need the medicine. Apparently they had a map that showed them where the mosquitoes hung out and mugged people. Then if they determined if you were going to an area on their map and you needed the medicine, they would give that to you or other preventative medicine precautions. So let's recap to ensure we are all picking up what's being put down. They want you to go down to medical for a screening to see if you need medicine that may or may not work. It takes a few days to get in your system, but they sent the information out in less than the time it took to get in your system (literally a few hours before). It only applies if you're leaving out of bounds, but there's no guarantee the medicine will do anything at all for you either, and you could possibly be wasting your time and expose yourself to the side effects, like explosive diarrhea. I'm glad they gave people enough time to take care of all that stuff, I mean, I'd hate to only have a day (not even) to take care of everything I needed to take care of before going out in town. However, I stayed in bounds though, so I didn't even see any mosquitos during my time there. But like anything else, extra measures are usually taken to ensure people stay safe. One of those measures I've seen used is the use of little green ID cards.

LIBERTY POSTER

C lose your eyes for a minute (after you read this of course) and imagine a world where you're on a cruise ship and need a liberty card (an extra form or ID generated by the cruise line) to get off the boat to go into the country you are visiting. The day before pulling in, not a moment sooner, they say we need to get these printed out but instead of giving you a liberty card, which can fit in your wallet and is usually the size of a credit card, they give you a liberty poster. An 8x11-card printout. I'm exaggerating, but it is huge, and tell you to keep this on you when you go in town. So after getting this card, there was a brief about the port visit. In this brief, imagine they show you a map of where you can go and then lay a fishing net over top of the map and say you can only go to the places the net doesn't touch but also you can't go to any of the places that are adjacent to anything that the net touches. And the main boundary line that tells you where you can't leave, you can't be touching anything on or near that line either. Oh, and by the way, the name of the port you are pulling into is not the actual place you're going, so all of you who made hotel reservation, you have to cancel. It's like going on a carnival cruise to the Bahamas, but when you pull in, you see signs that say welcome to Croatia or Berlin. When you get there, you're told you can only stay in the Beverly Hills of this place, so now you will pay more money to be there. Then the crime rate there was described as if it was the opening movie scene from the movie *Predator 2*. In places like this, you have to ensure your safety and not tell anyone where you are going next because people like Somalian pirates been stealing ships, but when you do a quick Google search and you see your ship is found on several news and media sites telling where you are going and when you will be there. It's like talking at a normal volume in someone's ear in a 5x5 elevator with five other people standing next to you and thinking you are telling a secret. Speaking of secrets, that reminds me about the guy who did some nasty stuff and didn't tell anyone, but everyone found out about it in the worst way.

DOO DOO HANDS

We all have those moments when our stomach feels as peaceful as birds chirping in a meadow as the old spice guy rides on a horse in the background whistling do-do do do do do-do do. Sometimes our stomachs are violent, like a hurricane sitting over an exploding volcano while buildings are blowing up and chaos and anarchy fill the streets. In this story, the guy was neither, he just had to use the bathroom. This is where our story takes a turn for the worst. As he entered the stall, he sat down and proceeded to relieve himself. Upon completing his mission, he didn't reach for toilet paper roll that was on the holder but instead he grabbed the roll that was free and handled by the masses. As he stuck his finger in the cardboard holder that keeps the paper together, he touched something that felt like mud, except this time it wasn't mud. Feeling personally victimized by the toilet paper roll because not only did he now have to wipe, but now he was confined to utilizing one arm while not touching anything else in the three-by-three stall. He still had to pull up his pants, zipper, and button them, and you can't do that with one hand. He now found himself trapped inside a shitty situation the phantom shitter had set. As the

James Wells

plot thickened, the look of disappointment and sadness on his face was similar to that kid that got a birthday card that didn't have any money in it. Finally after some wiggling and twisting, he was able to break free of his captor's tricks and escape. Luckily for him, there was actually soap in the bathroom this time.

NIGHT OF THE PHANTOM SHITTER

Phantoms are some of the pettiest and annoying paranormal phenomenon ever. The ones on the cruise ship, however, make the normal ones look about as goofy as a football bat. After a long hard day of non-stop strenuous work, all you want to do is take a shower and relax. This one guy started gathering his things and headed into the bathroom to clean up. What he would soon realize is the phantom shitter would claim its next victim. The guy, while never looking down (first mistake), hung up his towel, put his soap on the rack, and stepped into the shower. Immediately he started getting the shampoo lathered up while moving in circles in the shower (second mistake). His report said he kept kicking what he thought was his shampoo bottle (third mistake), and as he opened his eyes, he saw a dense turd and brown stuff all on his feet. With his poop feet, he jumped out the shower. If he would have jumped any faster, he would have caught up to yesterday. As he landed, the turd must have been on his shower shoes because it was now all over his leg, like honey on a hot biscuit. However, not all phantoms are created equal. Some like taking your laundry.

DIRTY SOCK BANDIT

D
on't you just hate it when the washing machine eats you socks and underwear and you don't find out until after the fact when you are folding and putting your clothes away, and at that point, you realize half your wardrobe is absent. Imagine how frustrated you would be if the socks and underwear from your dirty laundry bag went missing before you even made it to the laundry room. Apparently that's what happens when you go to sleep on a ship and have your dirty laundry bag hanging from a hook on the side of your bed. The dirty laundry fairy comes by and takes one of each sock, so you're left without any pairs, just singles and about a third of the underwear you own. To top it all off, the criminal doesn't even leave any money under your pillow. It's like going to the shoe store and buying a brand-new pair of shoes, and when you take a nap, someone comes in your house and only steals the left shoe out the box and closes it back up like nothing happened. This has to be on the same level of eating a banana and throwing the peel in the trashcan, and when you go to sleep, someone comes and takes the peel out of your trashcan but then flips over the trashcan and leaves the rest of the trash on the floor. Why steal dirty socks and under-

wear though; there is no way you are trying to save $9.98 that bad instead of getting some new ones. And the worst part is that they still have to wash them before wearing them. Unless they just threw them on straight out the laundry bag. Yuck, I'll give them the benefit of the doubt and hope they had a perfect soap to water mixture when they did wash their stolen clothes. As long as they read the directions on the laundry soap bottle, they should be fine, but sometimes the directions can be a little over the top if common sense isn't used in conjunction with them. Like the time the guy failed an exam for not knowing where the name of the room was located.

SEND HIM A BUCKET

magine a world that if you went through a door or up a ladder, you could not go back unless it was written on a paper somewhere, but it wasn't. Imagine you needed something telling you how much soap to mix with water to make soapy water to clean a wall, but it didn't tell you. Imagine you're in a building but can't prove you're in that building because it doesn't have the building's name anywhere. Imagine you're being graded on following all the directions on a pamphlet that only has half the information on it. There were directions to follow on a pamphlet, just like the one that comes with a dresser telling you how to put it together. It was telling people to go up a ladder and wipe off some stuff, but it never said come down the ladder after you were done. So the guy comes down because he was finished and failed his exam. Not sure what the inspector wanted him to do, just finish his work and then stay up there and never come down. Maybe send him up a couple hot plates and a piss bucket. Clearly this guy doesn't think to pull his head in before he shuts the window. So people got smart and realized things like this was happening and had to basically tell people to stop over analyzing and being extra, and most importantly, use your brain. That information was about as useful as a screen door on a submarine because it was still happening for a while afterwards. The one that got me was someone asked to add directions to the pamphlet for a specific amount of soap to add to a specific amount water to make soapy water because it just told you to use soapy water, and they didn't want to mess that up. Irish Springs doesn't tell you how much soap to add to your shower for you to get clean. Who sits there and measures out five fluid ounces of soap to fifteen of water? The answer... nobody. Clearly this guy was a few eggs short of a dozen. Seems like the wheel was spinning, but the hamster is dead. Sometimes it makes sense to have these things completely written out, so people don't hurt themselves like on bleach bottles but not soapy water.

THE BOX

ave you ever met a person and thought, man, this guy would need instructions on how to drain his shoe if it had water in it. I actually found that person. So there was a guy who was told to "go get a tri-wall," which is just a really big box, "and put these parts in it, so they are not lying on the floor." Mind you this box was already picked up and just sitting outside the shop patiently waiting to be put together, so that parts could be put in it.

Anyhow, the guy says, "Well, I don't know where the box is."

"How about you get up and go look," said the supervisor. So he went out in the shop and eventually found the box. So what did this guy do? I'm glad you asked. He sat the box right in front of a hurricane fan and put his paperwork on top of the box and walked off. Now I'm no rocket scientist, but something tells me that paper flies away when blown by a large fan. A few guys saw what is about to happen and tried to help him out. They looked at the papers, and the papers said things like do not touch and stay out. So the guys used a little common sense and said he must have been going to attach these to the box, so let's do it for him, so his papers don't fly away, and they stapled the papers to the box. Well, the guy came out furious about his papers, that he was going to attach to the box, were now attached to the box and he threw a temper tantrum comparable to a person with no hands trying to get a piece of food out their teeth. He then ripped the papers off the box and went back into the office. He came back out with reprinted papers that said the same thing as the ones on the box to begin with and stapled them to the box, along with another paper that stated if you touch, bump into, look at, or mess with this box, I will write you up. Mind you this box was right in the middle of the shop. So long story short, he was then called into the office and told to take those signs off the box. Meanwhile everyone that worked there was hanging off the side of the box, taking selfies with the box, and getting in the box and acting as if it was a sailboat. Seemed kind of childish but could have been a lot worse. They could have run around in a dinosaur costume in another country acting crazy.

ENTER THE DINOSAUR

While overseas any ship pulling into a foreign port is a really great way to bring two countries together and discuss various matters. As the ship was getting ready for a big show, throwing a party for the foreign dignitaries, and talking about various topics, everyone was on edge trying to ensure everything was perfect. Everyone, except this one guy. So as all the foreign diplomats, prime minister, and president of the other country was coming aboard, a dinosaur, of all things, came up from within the depths of the ship and started streaking through the hallways, making dinosaur mating call sounds. Security was able to tackle the vigilante dinosaur and detain it before he was able to cause an international incident. Not sure why he brought a T-rex costume on the ship in the first place, that's about as goofy as going to the doctor to get help for your drinking problem, then lying to him when he asks about your drink consumption. Alcohol can get you in a lot of trouble and have you doing things you normally wouldn't do. Liquid courage, as they call it, puts hair on your chest and strippers in your mouth.

HE DID WHAT TO THE STRIPPER?

Seeing the world is awesome; every country has their thing that when you see it, it just blows you away. Some things in those countries you have to taste to get that rich experience of culture and expand your palate. However, some things you should keep out of your mouth, like strippers. Strippers should never go in your mouth. While in Spain, a few guys who were exploring saw a flashing sign labelled The Moulin Rouge and decided that would be a great place to spend the evening. Upon entering the establishment, they found an experience they would soon remember for the rest of their lives. The saying, I wish I could un-see something, was taken to an entirely new level as all the strippers in the buildings were the size of refrigerators. There were big fridges, little fridges, mini fridges, you name it, they had it. While two of the guys were distraught and ready to exit the premises, one guy was having the time of his life. He was making it rain harder than a cow pissing on a flat rock. As the two guys approached him to save him from himself and get him out of there, a stripper started making it clap in his face. So as he stuck his semi-circular bald head in her butt, he decided he wanted to rim her enchilada. He licked her butt cleaner than a Sham-wow wiping up a spilled bowl of chili. You could tell afterwards by the look on his face she didn't taste like unicorns and sparkles. Looked like he just tasted a bag of old nickels and garlic flavored Greek yogurt. A few days went by, and the guy could barely talk as his throat was super sore. After a medical examination was conducted, gonorrhea of the throat sure would explain that painful throat. Gonorrhea can cause many issues in the brain and maybe even result in seizures. But do you want to know what can really get your body convulsing and shaking out of control...the sauce.

THE SAUCE

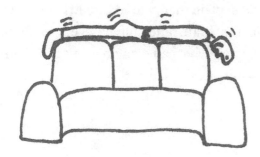

There's this guy who decided it would be a great idea to take some pre-workout from a guy who was five times his size and used what he liked to call "the sauce." He took half a scoop playing it safe, no big deal. Well, this stuff went through his system like Valvoline in a warm engine, just pumping him up. So trying to hit his workout harder than he normally does, he ran a few miles on the treadmill, threw in a good legs session, and then finished that up with about thirty minutes of an ab routine. I mean he was really getting it in. So after his workout, he took a shower and went to hang out with his roommates in the lounge. While he was in the lounge in his boxers, he started going into convulsions, looking as if he was trying to shake a can of soda. So instead of getting help from his roommates right next to him, he ran down the hall and told their other roommate to come look at how silly so and so looks in the lounge. The roommate came in and immediately called emergency services for help as the guy was now planking across the couch and shaking vigorously. You could have handed him anything and it would have been shaken up rather good. Soda, a paint can, a baby, it didn't matter. The medical team then came in and put this guy, half-naked and afraid, on a stretcher in only his underwear and took him to the medical treatment facility. Once he arrived at the hospital, they diagnosed his convulsions as a symptom of dehydration, gave him an IV, and sent him on his way. Gym stories are the best though. If you don't know what you're doing, please stay out until you learn how to properly do the work outs. Or at least wear something that makes you look like you know what you're doing.

YUCK, MEATBALLS

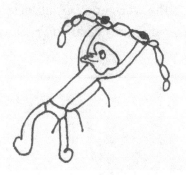

Do you even lift, bro? A friendly saying often said around the gym rats as a phrase to mess with a person less physically capable than they are. So what should any man that feels physically imposed on do? I can assure you it's no putting on you best pair of daisy duke swim shorts and going to the gym like this guy did. So as all the regulars are lifting and doing their thing as they normally would, this guy decides he wanted to do a chest day because when your shorts are as small and tight as his were, leg day is not even an option. So as the guy is looking goofy and lifting his weights, another guy happens to look over and sees what appears to be a human colored meatball hanging from the bottom of the guys shorts. Upon closer examination, it wasn't an actual meatball hanging out, but it was definitely some type of meat hanging out his shorts. This didn't stop the guy from getting his workout in. The big guy who saw the frank and beans hanging out yelled at the guy, who coincidently also happened to work for him, and made him leave and go change his clothes. Doing things like that will have you hemmed up in front of your boss and locked up in jail doing role call several times for indecent exposure.

TAKING ROLL CALL

S
ome people do things with a purpose behind it; other people do things just to do them. Like the guys who thought it would be a great idea to take roll call on everyone in jail, let them go back to their cells, and then take roll call on them again five minutes after everyone left. The reason was just to have everyone stand around for forty-five minutes, then let them go again. It's like asking your friend for a ride to the store for eggs. Then you wait till you get home to check the eggs and realize they are all broken. You wait a few minutes and call your friend back up, but now he's already comfortable and fourteen minutes deep into season three of *Gray's Anatomy*, and you ask them for another ride to the grocery store. But this time you get stuck in traffic for forty-seven minutes, and when you get back to the store, they are out of eggs. Regardless I would much rather be at a roll call than to be trapped with no escape in a room.

TRAPPED IN THE HALLWAY

From the people who brought you trapped in the closet comes trapped in the hallway. It's a story about a guy I ran into that found himself in a passageway that had two doors and two sets of steps, one that went up and one that went down, and nothing was locked. There was a door that he needed to go through to get to his place of domicile, and this door was kind of heavy, so you actually had to man up and push it to open it. Well, he didn't do that, and so I came walking down the steps into the room and saw him barely push on the door and then kind of step back a little bit and examine the door. Instead of me asking him to move, so I could open it, so everyone and go through. I said to myself nope, I want to see where this goes.

So he started examining the door like it was broken and said to me, "It looks like this hinge is broken, this is why the door is stuck." Mind you that broken piece had been like that since we left, so I knew that wasn't the problem. Then he looked at me and said, "Well, how do we get out of here," as if he just appeared in the space and didn't just walk up the steps to get there.

I looked at him and said, "Well, you could go down and around or up and over. Or we could just open the door." So after letting him freak out for a few minutes, I said excuse me, lifted the handle, gave it a good push, and opened the door. He was now no longer trapped and felt safe again. Sadly though not everybody can be rescued from themselves.

COULD YOU TEACH ME TO COMPUTER?

S o a guy was transferring doctor's offices and had to pick up his records. So he made his appointment and started talking to the clerk at the front desk. The clerk asked him for a hard copy of his transfer paperwork, which he didn't have on him at the time, so he asked if it would be ok if he emailed the digital one in his phone to her, and she agreed. He sent her the email with the attachment and she went in the back to grab it off the printer. About fifteen minutes later, she came back and said she received the email and can view the paperwork on the screen, but when she hits print, it keeps printing out a blank page. She shows him the paper she printed and then tells him that he will have to go and print it out because it's not working on their computers. After looking at the paper, the guy immediately realizes that the clerk printed out the blank email instead of the attachment. Not once, not twice, but three times she did this. He then told her to print the attachment and not the email. She had three chances to fix her mistake. This is like grabbing a hot pot off the stove and burning your hand, but you know you have to get the pot off the stove. So instead of turning off the heat and grabbing the pot holder, you leave the flame on the highest temperature and keep trying to grab the pot with your bare hands until you melt all your fingertips to the side of the pot. I guess emails can be confusing at times.

SPELLING ERRORS

One time an email was sent out from a frustrated individual who apparently lost something of his and would like someone to give it back. In his story, he talked about how he sat it down in the bathroom and how it has stickers on it, to which only he knew what the stickers were. Unless you're the person who took it, then you would also now know what the stickers looked like. But anyway, in his description, it also had a "Paracorde" attached. He would be "great fully" appreciated for its return. Then he leaves his signature at the bottom. While looking at the name, it is clear that something is not right. After further examination of the email that had several grammatical and spelling errors in it, it was concluded that he even misspelled his name in his signature. Now I know I don't proofread any of my stuff, as you can see from what you've read so far, and I may misspell words at times and things like that, but when the computer puts a little red squiggly under your name, you might want to make sure you fix that before sending that out to everyone on your contacts list. It's like typing up an email to your boss about how much you hate them and how you never want to see their face again. Instead of deleting the email, you hit send by accident, but it didn't just send to your boss. It somehow it made its way to all the local and national news channels who then decided to make it a headline and talk about it for thirty-seven minutes of the hour-long broadcast. Then while talking about it, they post a picture of the email up on the TV for everyone to read on the five o'clock news. All the while continuing to point out that you spelled your name wrong. To make matters worse, your boss is weird and likes to record the news on his DVR every night. It's ok to make silly mistakes sometimes, but some mistakes hold a little more weight than others.

FILLING THE TANK

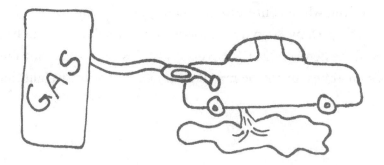

Imagine having a car but the fuel was so bad that you had to drain it all out and replace it with good fuel. Keep imagining as you remove the drain plug out from the bottom of it and watch as the fuel pours out into the pan. As the fuel begins to stop flowing, you are now ready to fill it back up, so you call a fuel truck to come by your building to give you fuel. You bring the car outside and park it over a sewer drain that leads to the ocean because why not. As the truck begins to fill the car up with gas, you begin to wait. Twenty minutes goes by and the car's fuel gage is still showing empty, but you know the car has been getting fuel for almost a half hour because you can smell it. Confused as to how this car is now holding over 1,000 gallons of fuel, you look underneath, and you immediately realize you forgot to put the plug back in to keep the fuel from coming out. The fuel was going from the truck through the car and straight to the storm drain. The fuel truck driver quickly shut off the fuel as people started rushing over to see what all the commotion was. As you hear a guy in the back mention EPA has been called, you see the driver of the fuel truck say how he forgot about a doctor's appointment he had to go to. So he jumped in his vehicle and disappeared faster than a donut at a police convention. Moral of the story, never trust a man wearing a Star-Kist Chunky Tuna Hat. Since we are still imagining having a liquid going straight through our cars, imagine a liquid going through a person. I want you to think of what comes to mind when you hear the word moist.

WET DREAMS

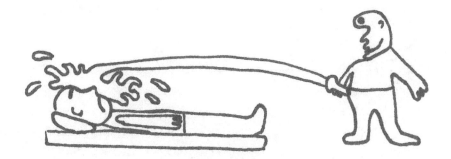

Close your eyes for a moment and imagine you are sound asleep in your two and half foot by six-foot box shaped bed. Now this is the most comfortable sleep you've had in a few days. Especially since you been dealing with the fuel leak from the other day. Imagine all those unicorns jumping over fences in your dreams when out of nowhere you wake up to another guy standing over you drunk and thinking you're a urinal. This guy had drunk so much alcohol that if you lit him on fire, he would have burned for five days. How he got to his room, we may never know. However, what we do know is that he thought he was pissing in a toilet before going to sleep, but he was really just getting another guy really moist. This is like the other day when your kid was sound asleep in your bed and had a dream that he was going to the bathroom and peed on you. I guess it was too much drinking and partying for someone who had a hard time holding their alcohol. Having fun and partying can be a lot of fun at times, especially on holidays when you can hang out with friends and pop bottles.

POPPIN BOTTLES

New Year's Eve celebrations on land is a time when people get dressed up with silly glasses, pull on blowout strings, and watch the ball drop. While out to sea on a cruise ship, you really don't have many options on what you can do to celebrate. One year they happened to have a small party on the ship with food and drinks. Not everything was eaten or drank, so a few people grabbed some of the sparkling cider bottles from the party because being some of the most responsible non-alcoholic people you will ever meet, that's what you do. Then they got this amazing idea and decided to go take the party to where they worked. One of the guys just couldn't figure out how to get his bottle to pop open, so he just kept shaking it as if he was in an infomercial selling shake weights for $19.95. Finally the bottle erupted like a Ron Jeremy training video, knocking the other guys hat off his head. Meanwhile the supervisor, who was about as confused as a Starbucks executive showing up in a wife beater for a conference call in Atlanta, was behind the door in her office and heard a lot of commotion going on in the other room. As she came out the office, she walked into total chaos. Alcohol, faker than Fox News, was all over the equipment, the ceiling, and people's clothes. Everyone was singing the old acquaintance song and swinging from the rafters, you get the picture. The supervisor at this point had completely lost her shit and sucked all the fun out of the atmosphere, like a black hole eating the soul of a dying star. She made everyone clean the shop for the rest of the night. Meanwhile people were still swinging from the ceiling, but they had mops and rags in their hands this time as they swept and mopped the ceiling and wiped down all the floors with rags. It's not always that fun working with other people. Sometimes you have to watch your back, or you can get seriously injured.

THE FIRE BOTTLE

You ever work with someone who tried to accidentally kill you on purpose with a fire extinguisher? Fire watches are people used to prevent something from catching on fire. Usually they stand watch with a fire extinguisher as a safety observer as another person is welding. The minimum requirement to be a fire watch is to be able to see a fire and then be able to put it out. Yep, that pretty much sums it up. Pretty sure a T-Mobile sales rep who can only sell gift cards and pop sockets requires more credentials. However, I am now convinced that the most difficult job in the world is figuring out how to get a fire extinguisher bottle from point A to point B without killing somebody. It literally requires an IQ equivalent to an empty tuna fish can, but somehow this happened.

To help the watch out, the leader of the operation tied the rope to the fire extinguisher and said, "When I get to the bottom, just drop this down there." Well, the lead guy gets down to the bottom and yells up for his helper to drop it down. And, boy, did this guy drop it down. He dropped the entire bottle down the hole, rope and all, nearly killing the guy at the bottom. The guy at the bottom even tied the rope to the fire extinguisher for the watch before he climbed down, all he had to do was lower it into the hole by the rope. Nope, he dropped that bottle down there like Hulk Hogan dropping his massive leg off the top ropes onto his opponent's neck. Straight up sent that bottle down with vengeance through the gates of hell, nearly decapitating the guy at the bottom.

The guy at the bottom, completely oblivious to what just occurred, asked the fire watch what happened, and the fire watch told him, "You said to drop it down." I'm not sure what else the supervisor would tie a rope to the bottle for... Looks? Maybe to make it look more distinguished, like a cartoon bomb, so he could submarine that thing down ten decks to put a crack in the earth. It's almost as bad as when the supply folks throw packages with the words fragile on the side of the box.

SHIPPING AND SUPPLY

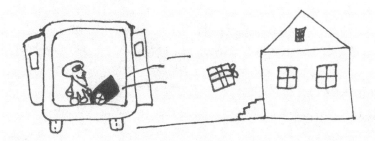

When it comes to getting packages sent out, nobody does it better than the guys who work in shipping and receiving. We all seen the videos. They expeditiously get your packages over a fence with their catapult-like devices hidden in the back of their trucks, and as the package smashes into the ground, you can only watch helplessly on your Ring camera as the side of the box that says fragile gets curled up like a fried piece of bacon. Or when you need to fix something that is leaking, so you order the seal needed for the repair and they staple the receipt to it, tearing a hole in the middle of the seal, rendering the item as useless as a box of smashed door knobs. However, what they really specialize in is returns and opening packages. Like when you order an inner tube to repair a flat tire and they decide to open the box up for you with their machete sized box cutter and end up slicing the box in half, along with half of the new inner tube you ordered. It could have been worse though. They could have decided to just put a bag on it and leave it there.

CAPTAIN SAVE-A-PIPE

W hile walking through the hallway one day, a guy noticed there was a pipe that was missing a section on the top and water was pouring out. There was water all over the floor, so he decided to mop it up. He tried to put a bucket under it to catch the water, but the way the pipes were shaped on the bottom, that wasn't going to happen. Curious as to why someone didn't just cut the water off when they removed a section of the pipe had him baffled. This is like removing the sink in your house without shutting the water off and then being confused as to why your living room floor is now covered in ten inches of water. So as the guy and his friend were standing there trying to figure out what to do in the meantime until the plumbers turned the water off on their end, another guy comes up and asks what they are doing. Meanwhile everyone was standing in a huge puddle looking up at the pipes. He suggested that they place a bag on the top of the pipe. Have you ever just looked at someone and started squinting like that is going to help you try to understand what they just said?

The guy and his friend said, "If we put a bag on this, then the bag is going to fill up with water, and then we are going to have an even bigger mess once the bag breaks or comes loose." He insisted that it wouldn't create a mess and it would stop the leak, so to prove a point, one of the guys grabbed a paper bag and placed it on top of the pipe. Simultaneously the plumbers had finally cut the water off, so it had now looked like the paper bag on top of the pipe had stopped the leak. The guy with the suggestion was so happy to hear that the bag stopped the leak and felt like he knew what he was talking about. But they let him continue to feel like Captain Save-a-Pipe and didn't say anything. Not all heroes wear capes and not all people are qualified for their jobs. This is why waiver programs are established in different companies. It's to help those who are capable of doing the job but not yet qualified where they currently are in their life. Hell, even some of the people who screen the waivers don't even know how to screen the paperwork, and that's how we end up running in circles.

WHERE'S THE WAIVER?

There was a guy who went to immigration and routed some paperwork that he needed to go to another country, but he needed a waiver form. So he put all the paperwork to include the waiver and routed it to the people who needed to see it. The paperwork was returned to him without it having the required signatures he needed from the people he gave it to. Why, do you ask? Well, attached to the waiver form was a posted note that said needs to also have a waiver form, with question marks all over it as if there wasn't a waiver to begin with. This is like losing your phone but the entire time it's in your hand. We could just lock these guys up and leave the key in the cell with them. I'm sure they still wouldn't figure out how to escape. The crazy part is one guy actually did have the code to a lock and still couldn't get the lock open.

OPENING A LOCK

A newly qualified inspector had a lock issued to him. When you go to change the numbers, there is a little tab sticks out, so you can change the numbers by spinning the tab. However, this guy decided it would be easier to stick his massive finger in the tiny window that the number was in and tried to change it that way. This is like a four-year-old getting his massive head stuck in the railing and wondering why he can't move or go anywhere. He sat there trying to get this lock to work for almost thirty minutes before accepting defeat. The lock came with instruction, but even with instructions, somethings require a little bit more. Some require tools, some require batteries, and some just require caution tape.

CAUTION, WET PAINT

With wet paint signs and caution tape all over the place, this one guy still managed to lean up against the wall, getting paint all over his hand. While leaving out the room, he decided to open the door with the same hand he touched the paint with. Smearing paint hands all over everything, like we all did as kids in kindergarten when we made our turkey pictures for Thanksgiving. At this point, all the doorknobs were now white with paint hands. Instead of cleaning the knobs off, all the knobs were replaced with new ones. This is like using the bathroom, and instead of flushing the toilet, you go to Home Depot and buy a new toilet because the one you just used is now dirty. Speaking of paint, do you know how long it would take you to sweep dried up paint drops off the ground? I don't either, but I was waiting to see how long it would take the guy to realize that they weren't going to come off the ground like that. This is like trying to sweep the sand off the beach. Maybe with enough muscle, he could have gotten them off the floor. Or broke something like a back-yard mechanic when they are trying to fix a lawnmower.

BACK YARD MECHANIC

You ever take your car to the mechanic for a simple fix to a problem, and when you get your car back, you can't drive it away because it doesn't work anymore. So there's a tractor that came in the shop with a simple issue. All that was needed to fix the issue was a few bolts tightened on the engine and that was it. Well, the bolts did get tightened. In fact they got tightened so tight that the bolt snapped in half like a toenail when you hit your foot on the side of the couch. The part that was broken took nine months to come in after being ordered. The guy who tightened the bolt with the force of fifteen men made it known before he started working on the tractor that he used to be a mechanic and worked on cars since he was three-years-old. Just so we are clear, losing your father's tools in the garage is not the same as you fixing a car when you're three-years-old. This same guy later decided he would change out a drum of hydraulic oil to work on some other equipment. Problem is not all hydraulic fluid is the same. Instead of looking at the label to make sure he had the right stuff, he changed out the red barrel for the yellow barrel. This is like you buying a crib set for your kid but decided to not look at the instructions.

And because of your extensive knowledge in carpentry, you ended up building a coffee table instead. Talking about breaking all these nuts reminds me about an air duster can for some reason.

CAN OF DUSTER

Awell-respected supervisor walked into a bathroom to check on his guys as they were cleaning up the bathroom. As he walked around looking for his guys, one of them happened to be missing. As the supervisor started to walk out the bathroom, he heard a ssshhhrrtttt sound, followed by a thud in one of the stalls. He peeked through the bathroom stall door and he saw his missing guy passed out on the toilet. He was leaning against the toilet paper dispenser with a can of air duster in one hand and his genitals in the other. This guy clearly was not cleaning the bathroom like he was supposed to be doing. The supervisor had called the medical staff, meanwhile the CEO happened to be conveniently walking by the bathroom and heard a bunch of commotion, so he poked his head in and saw this event unfolding. Imagine sitting on a toilet, sniffing an aerosol can, passing out while holding your junk in the other hand and waking up to your boss and a bunch of medical people standing over you. It definitely looked as bad as it sounds. The medical team ended up taking the guy away after they pried the duster can from his half-numb hand. I don't know what was worse, him trying to see what canned air smells like or him occupying a stall someone else could have used. There was a guy who needed to use a stall so bad one time, it sounded like a herd of elephants coming into the bathroom. The guy literally had burst in to the stall and went to sit down on the toilet, came in too hot, cracked the toilet seat in half, and butt mud shot out of him like a bullet and hit the floor behind the toilet. It was found a day later as they were cleaning up when the mop pulled it from behind the toilet leaving behind a long skid mark on the floor. Looked like someone was riding their bike real fast and slammed on the brakes. This was almost as nasty as that female dorm room I walked past that smelled like raviolis. All this ravioli talk got me feeling a little hungry. Maybe we should take a break and go get something to eat.

COMMON CORE

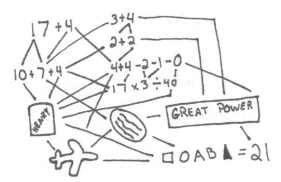

Have you ever gone through a restaurant drive thru and handed the cashier some paper money instead of a card and watched them common core math? First let's identify what common core math is. Common core math is when you take the long unnecessary way to figure out a simple problem. For instance let's take the problem ten plus ten. Seems easy, straightforward, and equals twenty. After applying common core, we will now cut the first ten in half and add it to the watermelon that was hiding behind the helicopter brake and then take fifteen because...why not. Where we got the fifteen, I don't know, but we will take that and multiply that by twenty-two because with great power comes great responsibility, plus thirty jars of Henrys divided by the nearest Walmart equals twenty. This way of thinking was designed to help the young generation problem solve better. Let's look at an example of just how well common core is applied in actual time. So after driving through the drive-thru, the total amount was $6.69. The cashier was handed $6 in paper bills and three quarters ($6.75), which covered the cost and the customer should have gotten $.06 back.

The cashier took the money, closed her window, and before

handing the customer their food, she said, "Do you have another quarter?" Now with a confused look on his face, and thinking to himself, I just gave you enough to cover the cost, she's about to jack this up. Sure, and he gave her another quarter. She then handed him his change, the $.06 cents originally owed to him plus a different quarter. This is about as goofy as saying you're going to take a break from the internet on your computer and then you go and look at the internet on your phone. Glad that lunch math problem is over, and just like all good things, it must come to an end.

WALKING PAPERS

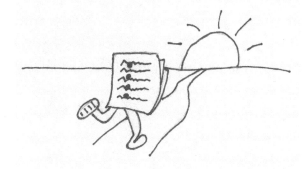

S
o I received my walking papers, and as I walked off into the sunset for the last time, I felt a heavy bag lifted off my shoulders. Shortly after I grabbed another really heavy bag and carried it to the airport. The phrase bittersweet came to mind at times, but nothing was bitter about any of it, only the sweet taste of victory. I have seen things and heard stories of some of the craziest things imaginable and now you have, too. I've seen a man jump off the tenth floor of a hotel and into a three foot pool breaking just about every bone in his body. I've seen a guy get locked in a hallway, a guy swimming in the ocean waiting for his boat. I know a man who busted his head wide open while reaching for that last ice cream in the store, nearly rendering himself unconscious. A man who just couldn't wake up on time, one that couldn't iron, one that could iron but did it while wearing his clothes. I've traveled around the world, and along the way, I have met some really cool people, some who I'll have a bond with for the rest of my life and some who I may forget by the time I'm done writing this book. As I move on to my next adventure, I'm sure there will be several new stories to talk about, and I'm sure we will all get a kick out of them as well. But until then, this

chapter is closed, and I really appreciate you guys taking the time out to read my stories, and I hope you enjoyed this book.

CPSIA information can be obtained
at www.ICGtesting.com
Printed in the USA
BVHW041557060521
606653BV00012B/1981

9 781649 130525